UNDER THE SEA

Contents

Jan Burchett
and Sara Vogler

Story illustrated by
Martin Aston

Heinemann

Before Reading

Find out about

- The strange creatures that live in the deep dark sea

Tricky words

- leafy
- weird
- scary
- gobbles
- pufferfish
- anglerfish

Introduce these tricky words and help the reader when they come across them later!

Text starter

If you explore in the deep dark sea, you will find all sorts of sea creatures. Some are funny. Some are weird. Some are scary. Imagine you are in a submarine. You could meet a leafy sea dragon or a giant deep sea spider.

Funny, Weird and Scary

Leafy sea dragon

The leafy sea dragon lives in the deep dark sea.

It does not swim very fast.

If a big fish wants to eat it, the leafy sea dragon hides.

Is it funny, weird or scary?

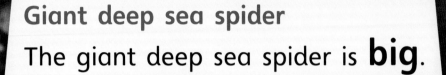

Giant deep sea spider

The giant deep sea spider is **big**.

It has a very long nose.
It gobbles its food up its nose.

It's as big as a large plate!

nose

Is it funny, weird or scary?

Pufferfish

The pufferfish is ugly.

If a big fish wants to eat it, the pufferfish puffs up with water.

Now the big fish does not want to eat it.

Is it funny, weird or scary?

Anglerfish

The anglerfish lives in the deep dark sea.

It has a light on its head.
Small fish swim to the light and the anglerfish gobbles them up!

Is it funny, weird or scary?

Hammerhead shark

The hammerhead shark is very big and it looks very ugly. It looks as if it has swum into a wall!

Is it funny, weird or scary?

head

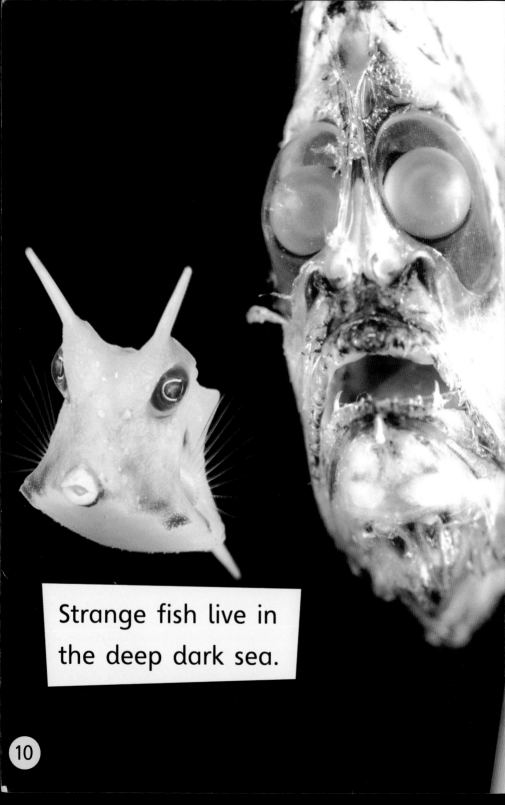

Strange fish live in the deep dark sea.

Quiz

Text Detective

- How does the giant deep sea spider eat?
- Would you like to meet any of these strange fish?

Word Detective

- **Phonic Focus:** Initial consonant clusters

  Page 8: What are the two phonemes (sounds) at the beginning of 'swim'? Can you blend them?
- Page 4: Find a word that means 'eats quickly'.
- Page 8: Find a word that rhymes with 'night'.

Super Speller

Read these words:

funny   lives   light

Now try to spell them!

HA! HA! HA!

Q Why was the crab arrested?

A Because it kept pinching things.

11

In this story

 Jack A big shark

Tricky words

- explore
- wreck
- submarine
- diving suit
- treasure
- something
- shoulder

Introduce these tricky words and help the reader when they come across them later!

Story starter

Jack was just an ordinary boy, but he had a magic backpack. When Jack pulled the cord on his backpack – Pop! – something magic popped out. One day, Jack was reading about shipwrecks.

Jack and the Wreck

"I want to explore a wreck," said Jack.

"I'll get my backpack and look for a wreck."

Jack went to the sea.

POP! Out of his backpack came a submarine.
Jack got into the submarine.

The submarine went into the sea.
Jack saw lots of fish.

Then Jack saw a wreck.
"I want to explore the wreck,"
he said.

In the submarine there was
a diving suit. Jack put it on.

Jack got out of the submarine.

He went into the wreck.

He saw a treasure chest.

"YIPPEE!" said Jack.

But Jack could not open the chest.

"I have not got a key," he said.

Something tapped Jack on the shoulder. It gave him a key.

"Thanks," said Jack.

What gave Jack the key?

19

Jack opened the chest.
It was full of treasure.

Something tapped him
on the shoulder.
It gave him a sack.

"Thanks," said Jack.

Jack looked at the sack.

He looked at the key.

Jack got into the submarine and zoomed away.

Quiz

Text Detective

- What did Jack find in the wreck?
- What would you have done if you had seen the shark?

Word Detective

- **Phonic Focus:** Initial consonant clusters

  Page 17: What are the two phonemes (sounds) at the beginning of 'treasure'? Can you blend them?
- Page 19: Find a word that means 'touched'.
- Page 23: Find a word with three syllables.

Super Speller

Read these words:

open   over   lots

Now try to spell them!

HA! HA! HA!

 Why was the sand wet?

A Because the sea weed.